The Secret Life of Bees

Sue Monk Kidd

STUDENT PACKET

NOTE:

The trade book edition of the novel used to prepare this guide is found in the Novel Units catalog and on the Novel Units website. Using other editions may have varied page references.

Please note: We have assigned Interest Levels based on our knowledge of the themes and ideas of the books included in the Novel Units sets, however, please assess the appropriateness of this novel or trade book for the age level and maturity of your students prior to reading with them. You know your students best!

ISBN 978-1-56137-025-2

To order, contact your local school supply store, or:

Toll-Free Fax: 877.716.7272
Phone: 888.650.4224
3901 Union Blvd., Suite 155
St. Louis, MO 63115

sales@novelunits.com

novelunits.com

Name _____

Clue Search

Directions: Collect information about the book for each of the items. Write down the information, and then make some predictions about the book.

Information Source	Information Provided
Dedication	
Title	
Cover Illustration	
Teasers on the cover	
Friends' recommendations	
Reviewers' recommendations/awards won	

Your predictions about the book:

Name _____

Directions: On a scale of 0–5, rate your knowledge of the following terms/events, with 0 indicating no familiarity and 5 indicating a great deal of familiarity. Choose one item, and write two or three sentences explaining what you would like to know about it and why.

_____ Beekeeping

_____ Bee colonies

_____ Segregation in the South prior to 1964

_____ The Civil Rights Act of 1964

_____ Ku Klux Klan

_____ Murders of three civil rights workers in Mississippi (1964)

_____ Deaths of four children in church bombing in Birmingham, Alabama (1963)

_____ Black Madonna

_____ Jewish Wailing Wall

_____ Feast of the Assumption

_____

_____

_____

_____

_____

Name _____

Word Map

presumptuous	imbecile	parsonage	pious
paradise	philosophy	decapitate	blaspheme
insomniac	oblivious	brazen	anointed
conjure	motes	wrench	

Directions: Complete the following chart for five of the vocabulary words. Share your finished charts with the class.

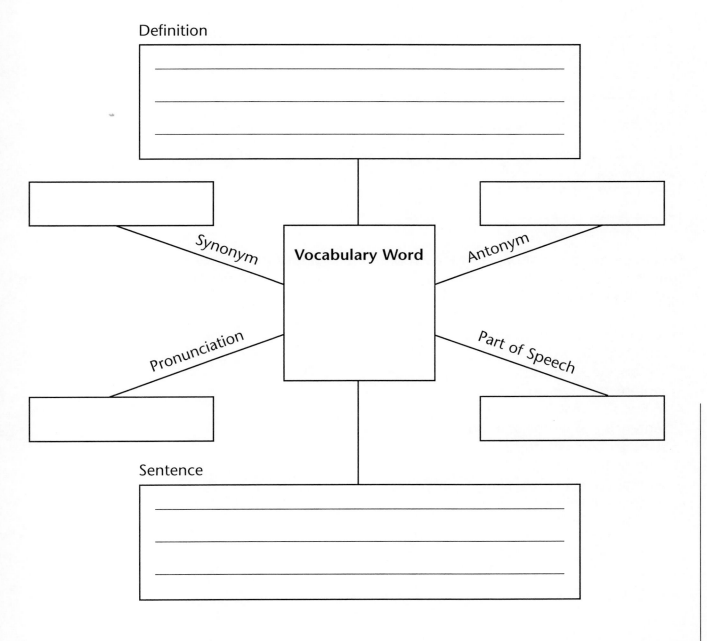

Definition

Synonym   Vocabulary Word   Antonym

Pronunciation   Part of Speech

Sentence

Name _____

pith	meander	bona fide	ingenious
sixth sense	consolation	vigilante groups	premises
corrugated	ambrosia	orthodox	solace
paranoid	naive	eclectic	cloister
bordello	consignment	mites	deciduous

Directions: Choose 15 vocabulary words from the list above. Write the words on the numbered lines below.

1. _____   2. _____

3. _____   4. _____

5. _____   6. _____

7. _____   8. _____

9. _____   10. _____

11. _____   12. _____

13. _____   14. _____

15. _____

On a separate sheet of paper, use each of the following sets of words in an original sentence. Your sentences should show that you know the meanings of the vocabulary words as they are used in the story.

Sentence 1: words 8 and 4
Sentence 2: words 9 and 3
Sentence 3: words 1 and 10
Sentence 4: words 11 and 7
Sentence 5: words 15 and 13
Sentence 6: words 3 and 6
Sentence 7: words 12 and 4
Sentence 8: words 14 and 9
Sentence 9: words 5 and 2
Sentence 10: words 7 and 6

© Novel Units, Inc.

Name _____

Crossword Puzzle

monogram	integrate	oblivious	catcall
siesta	minuscule	cunning	loping
stamen	nymphs	limbo	induction
sidled	dander	animation	catacombs
taffeta			

Directions: Select ten vocabulary words from above. Create a crossword puzzle answer key by filling in the grid below. Be sure to number the squares for each word. Blacken any spaces not used by the letters. Then, write clues to the crossword puzzle. Number the clues to match the numbers in the squares. The teacher will give each student a blank grid. Make a blank copy of your crossword puzzle for other students to answer. Exchange your clues with someone else, and solve the blank puzzle s/he gives you. Check the completed puzzles with the answer keys.

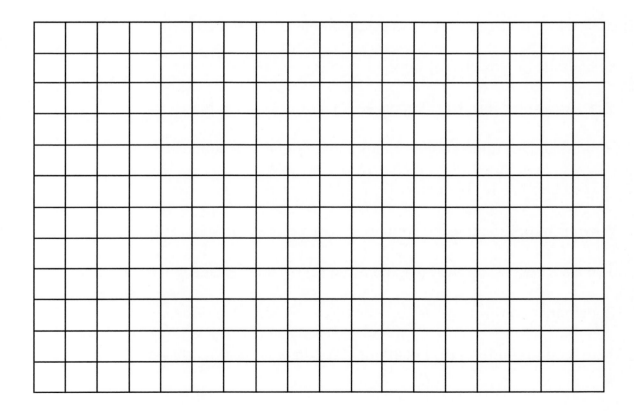

Name _____

industrious	exorcism	apiary	embalm
mull	shackled	bolstered	melancholy
sauntered	neurotic	contemptible	demoralized
trolling			

Directions: Choose the word or phrase closest in meaning to the vocabulary word as it is used in the book. Then use at least seven of the words in a poem or paragraph on a separate sheet of paper.

_____ 1. industrious (a) lazy (b) diligent (c) negligent (d) absurd

_____ 2. mull (a) crush (b) forget (c) seize (d) ponder

_____ 3. sauntered (a) strolled (b) dashed (c) sustained (d) soldered

_____ 4. exorcism (a) insertion (b) announcement (c) denigration (d) removal

_____ 5. shackled (a) freed (b) bound (c) dreamed (d) unsecured

_____ 6. neurotic (a) anxious (b) unconcerned (c) neutral (d) innovative

_____ 7. apiary (a) habitat (b) chimpanzee (c) atmosphere (d) hovel

_____ 8. bolstered (a) undermined (b) cushioned (c) fled (d) supported

_____ 9. contemptible (a) temporary (b) noble (c) despicable (d) graceful

_____10. embalm (a) preserve (b) comfort (c) release (d) proclaim

_____11. melancholy (a) relieved (b) depressed (c) blissful (d) tired

_____12. demoralized (a) sanguine (b) ethical (c) optimistic (d) disheartened

_____13. trolling (a) pushing (b) finding gold (c) dreaming (d) patrolling

Name _____

Directions: Answer the following questions on a separate sheet of paper. Use your answers in class discussions, for writing assignments, and to review for tests. Starred questions indicate thought or opinion questions.

Chapter 1

1. Identify the protagonist/narrator and the setting.

2. When do the bees arrive in Lily's room? Why is the timing of their arrival significant to Lily? Why does she think they have come?

3. *Quote Rosaleen's superstition about bees swarming. What does Lily think this means? Have you ever heard a superstition that you felt applied to you? If so, briefly explain why.

4. Who is Lily's father? How does she feel about him, and why doesn't she call him "Dad"? Give two examples of how he neglects or is cruel to her.

5. *Briefly explain Lily's first and only memory of her mother. What caused her mother's death? Why does Lily blame herself? Explain whether you think Lily is actually responsible.

6. Why does Lily feel that she is not and never will be popular? What does she think will give her a chance to overcome this? Why does this fail to materialize?

7. Who is Rosaleen? How does Lily feel about her? What does Lily daydream about her?

8. *How does T. Ray react when Lily asks about her mother? What mementoes of her does Lily have? Where does she keep them? Which one of these do you think is most important to Lily? Why?

9. *Identify Mrs. Henry, and briefly explain her effect on Lily. Identify a teacher who has positively influenced your life, and explain why you chose this person.

10. Why does Lily go to the orchard after T. Ray ignores her when she mentions her birthday? What happens because of this?

11. What is T. Ray's favorite way to punish Lily? How does Rosaleen react to this?

12. Why does Rosaleen go to town? Why is she arrested?

13. *Prediction: What will happen to Lily and Rosaleen?

Chapters 2–3

1. What happens to Rosaleen after she is arrested? Why doesn't Shoe protect her?

2. *How does T. Ray deal with Lily after Rosaleen's arrest? What is Lily's primary concern? How does she react to T. Ray's threat? Why do you think she stands up to him?

3. What does T. Ray tell Lily about her mother? How does Lily respond?

4. Look up the word "epiphany," and correlate with Lily's hearing a voice saying, "Lily Melissa Owens, your jar is open" (p. 41).

5. Give two reasons Lily decides to leave Sylvan. Why does she decide to go to Tiburon?

6. *Why is Brother Gerald going to the jail? What does Lily tell him about Rosaleen? Do you think he changes his mind about Rosaleen?

7. What does Lily discover about Rosaleen when she gets to the jail? Briefly explain what she does then and how Rosaleen reacts.

8. How do Lily and Rosaleen get to Tiburon? Why do they argue? How is their conflict resolved?

9. Where does Lily get food for her and Rosaleen? What does she steal? Why?

10. Who is August Boatwright, and what is her association with the picture of the Black Madonna?

11. **Prediction:** How will August Boatwright react to the arrival of Lily and Rosaleen?

Chapters 4–5
1. *Give two characteristics for each of the Boatwright sisters: (a) August (b) June (c) May. Which one do you think is the matriarch of the family? Why?

2. *Briefly describe the statue of the black Mary. How does the statue make Lily feel? What does May call the statue? What do you think this name signifies?

3. *Briefly summarize Lily's explanation of Rosaleen's injuries and why they have come to Tiburon. Explain whether you think August believes her tale.

4. Where do Lily and Rosaleen stay after they come to the Boatwrights' home? What job does August assign to each of them? How does Lily feel about staying here?

5. Why are the Boatwright sisters named after months of the year? Who was April, and what happened to her?

6. What does Lily ask Rosaleen not to mention to August? Why does she do this?

7. *Identify "May's wall," and answer the following questions: (a) What song does May hum just before going to her wall? (b) What does Lily discover in the wall? (c) Why did June and August come up with the idea of the wall? (d) What do you think the wall symbolizes?

8. *How does June feel about Lily and Rosaleen? How does August respond to these concerns? What other issues do you think influence June's viewpoint?

9. How does August explain the Boatwright sisters' religion? How does Lily react to their beliefs?

Chapters 6–7

1. Who is Neil? Why won't June marry him? How does this affect May?

2. Who are the Daughters of Mary? Who organized them?

3. In the story of "Our Lady of Chains": (a) Who is Obadiah? (b) What does he find? (c) What does he think this means? (d) What does he do with it? (e) Who does Pearl think the statue is? (f) Why do the slaves call her "Our Lady of Chains?"

4. *What causes Lily to faint? How does this affect everyone at the meeting? What does Lily resolve to do? Why do you think this is so important to her?

5. Who is Zach? What does he aspire to be? How do he and Lily interact?

6. *What keeps Lily from telling August the truth about her mother? Why do you think this is so important to Lily?

7. What emotions does Lily display when she and Zach go to harvest the honey? Why does she act this way?

8. Why does Rosaleen move out of the honey house? How does this affect Lily?

9. *What happens between June and Neil that causes May to go to her wall? Why do you think this situation affects her so intensely?

10. What gift does Zach bring to Lily? Why does he believe that they cannot have a romantic relationship?

Chapter 8

1. What is the name of the Black Madonna August puts on each jar of honey? How did August first become interested in the Black Madonna? Why does August put her picture on the honey?

2. *Name three things that Lily tells August she loves. Then name two things that she will not mention to August. Why do you think Lily is still reluctant to talk about her mother?

3. How long has August been keeping bees? Who taught her the trade? What did she do before she became a beekeeper?

4. *To what is August referring when she says, "The hardest thing on earth is choosing what matters" (p. 147)? What do you think this reveals about her?

5. Name the types of bees that make up a healthy hive. Why is the queen bee called "the mother of thousands?"

6. *What does Lily do to keep from getting stung by the bees? What does she think the bees are doing for her? Why do you think this is important to her?

7. What rumor is circulating around Tiburon? How do the townspeople react?

8. Who is Clayton Forrest? Why is Zach going to his office? How does his secretary react when she finds out that Lily is staying with the Boatwrights?

9. *How does Lily get in touch with her father? How does he react? What do you think will result from this contact?

10. *Briefly summarize the contents of Lily's letter to T. Ray. Why do you think she tears it up?

11. *Name three requests Lily makes in her prayer to Our Lady of Chains. Which one do you think is the most significant? Why?

Chapter 9
1. What is Lily's "initiation" into beekeeping?

2. Who starts the frolic in the water? What is the result for June and Lily?

3. *To what does Lily compare her thoughts? What do you think she means about wearing a "necklace of lies?"

4. What makes Lily realize that her mother has been in the Boatwrights' home? How does she react?

5. What causes Lily to become "a case of nerves" (p. 175)? What does she decide to do? What keeps her from doing this?

6. What day of the week do Zach and Lily go to town? Why is this significant?

7. Why is Zach arrested? What does Lily do? How does August react to Zach's arrest?

8. *Why doesn't anyone tell May about Zach's arrest? Explain why you do or do not think this is a wise decision.

9. *Who goes to visit Zach in jail? What does Lily promise him she will do? Why do you think she does this?

10. How does May find out about Zach's arrest? What is her reaction?

11. **Prediction:** What will happen to May?

Chapter 10
1. Where do August and the others go to search for May? What does August send June to do?

2. Where do they find May? What indicates she committed suicide?

3. How do the following people react to May's death: Lily, August and June, and Rosaleen? What does Lily believe caused May to commit suicide?

4. *Explain what you think Lily means when she says, "I was breaking every rule of successful lying" (196).

5. How does Mr. Hazelwurst reveal his racial prejudice while he is questioning Lily?

6. What is a vigil? Why does August think it is important to do this for May?

7. What happens that allows Zach to be released from jail? How has jail changed him?

8. *Why does Zach feel responsible for May's death? How does August respond to his self-recrimination? Do you agree or disagree with August?

9. *What is the significance of draping the hives? How do you think this relates to the saying, "When a bee flies, a soul will rise"?

10. What makes Lily feel that she is truly accepted by the Daughters of Mary? What does this make her decide is a "better plan?"

11. *Who finds May's suicide note? What reason does she give for committing suicide? Explain what you think she means by her statement, "…it's your time to live" (p. 210).

12. *How long does the vigil last? What does August then ask Zach and Lily to do? Why do you think this is significant to Lily?

Chapters 11–12

1. After May's funeral, what keeps Lily from telling August about her mother?

2. *What is Zach's "solution" to racial strife? How do you feel about the changes Zach's personality has undergone?

3. How long does the mourning period for May last? What is the sign to Lily that things are getting back to normal? What does Lily then decide to do?

4. How do the Boatwright sisters and the other Daughters of Mary adapt the Feast of the Assumption to their religion? What does the "feast" reveal about Lily's relationship with June?

5. *How does June's relationship with Neil change? Why do you think this happens?

6. How do the Daughters of Mary reenact the story of Our Lady of Chains? Where do Zach and Lily go after they watch this ceremony? What memory does this trigger for Lily? What does Zach tell Lily about how being arrested has changed him?

7. *Briefly explain Lily's emotions while waiting to talk to August, and name three things she learns about her mother. Which one do you think is the most important to Lily? Why?

8. What causes the "wall of glass" to break in Lily's chest? How does August react?

9. How does Lily feel about herself? Why? How does August respond?

10. *Why did Lily's mother come to Tiburon shortly before her death? What do you think could explain Deborah's actions?

11. Why does Lily say she hates her mother? What does August tell her that softens her opinion of Deborah?

12. *What phrase does Lily hear repeatedly in her mind? Do you agree with Lily that "knowing can be a curse on a person's life" (p. 255)?

Chapters 13–14

1. *What does Lily's anger toward her mother cause her to do? How does she feel afterward? Explain whether you think her actions are justified.

2. Who helps Lily clean up the mess in the honey house? How does Lily explain her actions? What does Rosaleen tell her about her mother?

3. If Lily could have one miracle from the Bible happen to her, what would she choose? Why?

4. What are the contents of the box August brings to Lily? Which of these items is most significant to Lily? Why is it so important to her?

5. *To what does Lily compare her heart? What do you think this implies?

6. *Explain whether you agree or disagree with Lily's opinion, "People, in general, would rather die than forgive" (p. 277). Whom is Lily having trouble forgiving?

7. *What does Lily do with her mother's things and the mouse's bones? What do you think this symbolizes?

8. How does August explain Our Lady to Lily?

9. How does T. Ray find Lily? Why has he come to Tiburon? Why does he call her by her mother's name? How does Lily respond?

10. How does August convince T. Ray to allow Lily to stay with her?

11. *What is Lily's final question for her father? What is his reply? Explain whether you think his answer is truthful.

12. Briefly explain the significance of each of the following in Lily's life following T. Ray's departure: (a) her belief in the "goodness of imagination" (b) charges against Rosaleen and Lily in Sylvan (c) Becca (d) the "moons" shining over Lily.

Name _____

Feelings

Directions: Complete the chart below for Lily Owens.

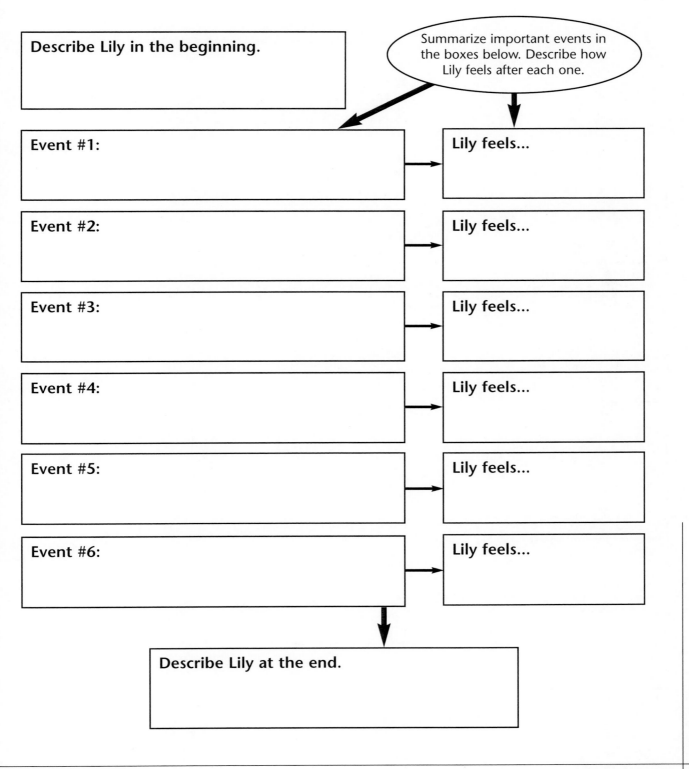

Describe Lily in the beginning.

Summarize important events in the boxes below. Describe how Lily feels after each one.

Event #1:

Lily feels...

Event #2:

Lily feels...

Event #3:

Lily feels...

Event #4:

Lily feels...

Event #5:

Lily feels...

Event #6:

Lily feels...

Describe Lily at the end.

Sequence

Directions: List the sequential steps in Lily's quest for forgiveness/acceptance.

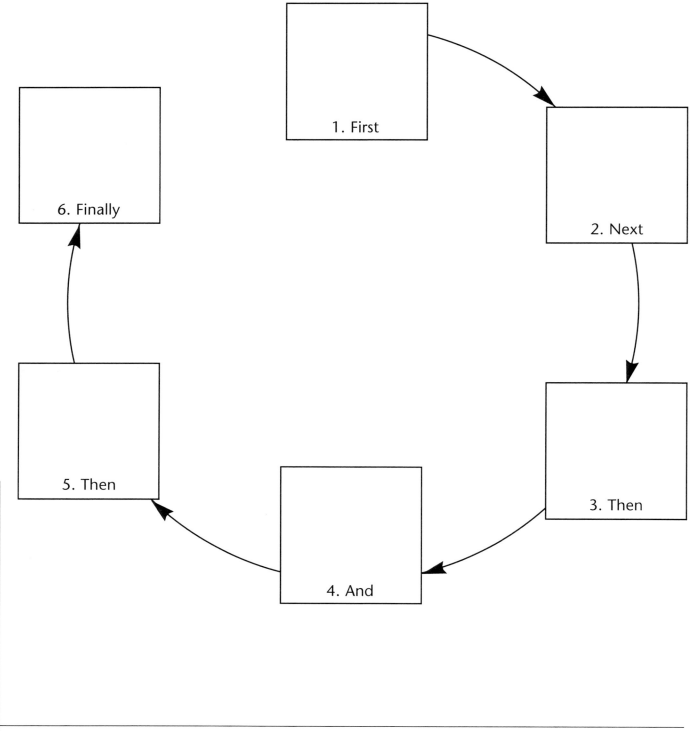

Name _____

Sociogram

Directions: On the "spokes" surrounding each character's name, write several adjectives that describe that character. On the arrows joining one character to another, write a description of the relationship between the two characters.

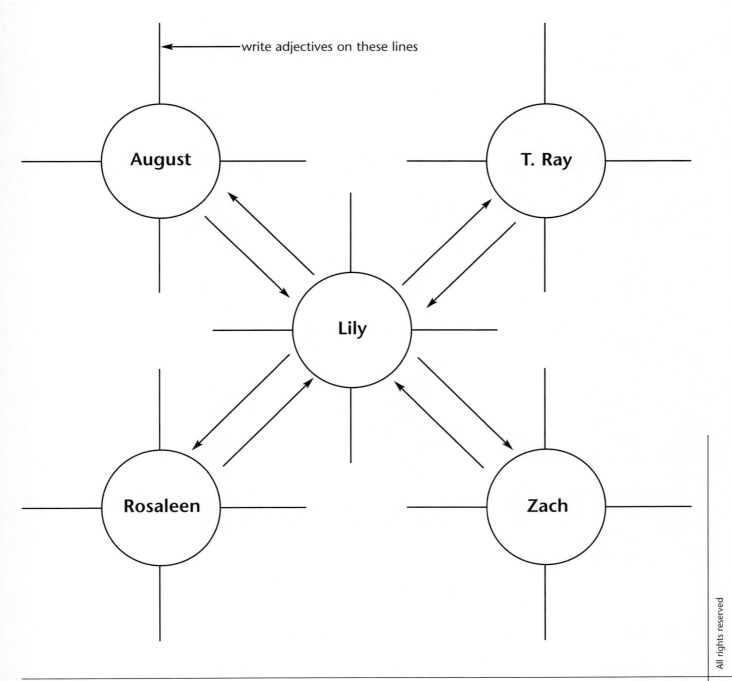

write adjectives on these lines

August

T. Ray

Lily

Rosaleen

Zach

Name _____

Cause/Effect Map

Directions: In each box, list a cause for Lily's low self-esteem.

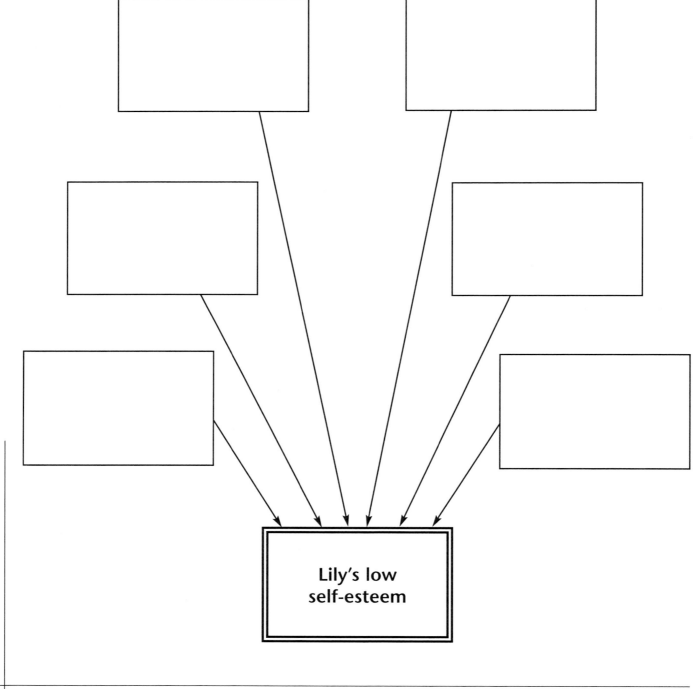

Name _____

Conflict

The **conflict** of a story is the struggle between two people or two forces. There are three main types of conflict: person vs. person, person vs. nature or society, and person vs. self.

Directions: The characters experience some conflicts in the story. In the chart below, list the names of three major characters. In the space provided, list a conflict each character experiences. Then explain how each conflict is resolved in the story.

Character:

Conflict	Resolution

Character:

Conflict	Resolution

Character:

Conflict	Resolution

Solving Problems

Directions: List six problems the characters in the novel face. Then complete the rest of the chart. For each problem, circle which solution you think is best—yours or the character's.

Problem	Character's Solution	Your Solution

Name _____

Story Map

Directions: Complete the following chart to show the novel's plot development.

Characters _____

_____

Setting

Time and Place _____

_____

Problem

Problem _____

_____

_____

Goal

Goal _____

_____

_____

Beginning ⟶ Development ⟶ Outcome

Episodes

_____

_____

_____

_____

Resolution _____

Resolution

_____

_____

_____

Name _____

Bio-poem

Directions: Using the format below, write a bio-poem about Lily Owens. Then write a bio-poem about yourself using the same format. Write a paragraph describing the values and characteristics you share.

—Line 1: First name only
—Line 2: Lover of (list three things character loves)
—Line 3: Giver of (list three things character gives)
—Line 4: Needs (list three things character needs)
—Line 5: Wants (list three things character wants)
—Line 6: Is good at (list three things character is good at)
—Line 7: Should work on (list three things character needs to improve)
—Line 8: Is similar to (list three people or other characters to whom this character is similar and list a reason behind each character)
—Line 9: Survivor of (list three things the character survives)
—Line 10: Last name only

Title _____

1. _____

2. _____

3. _____

4. _____

5. _____

6. _____

7. _____

8. _____

9. _____

10. _____

Thematic Analysis

Directions: Choose a theme from the book to be the focus of your word web. Complete the web, and then answer the question in each starred box.

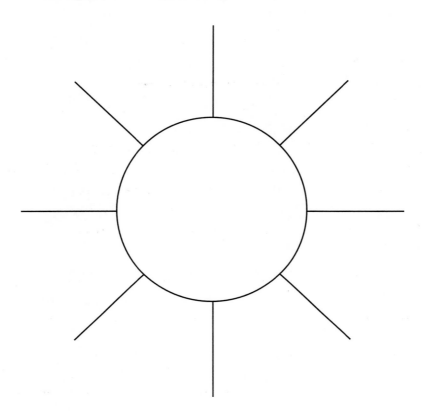

 What is the author's
main message?

 What did you learn
from the book?

Name _____

A. Sequence: Place the following events in chronological order.

_____ 1. T. Ray makes Lily kneel on grits because he thinks she's been with a boy in the orchard.

_____ 2. Lily chooses Tiburon as her and Rosaleen's destination.

_____ 3. Lily's mother dies.

_____ 4. Rosaleen pours snuff juice on the shoes of three racists.

_____ 5. Lily finds a paper bag containing some of her mother's things.

B. True/False

_____ 6. Lily's first memory of her mother is waking up and finding her gone.

_____ 7. Rosaleen is arrested on her way to register to vote.

_____ 8. Lily believes that she caused her mother's death.

_____ 9. In Sylvan Lily usually hides her mother's things under her bed.

_____ 10. Mrs. Henry tells Lily that she does not have the skills to become a writer.

C. Open-Ended Comprehension: On the lines below, explain the significance of Lily's epiphany, "Lily Melissa Owens, your jar is open."

_____

_____

_____

_____

_____

_____

_____

Name _____

A. Fill in the Blanks

1. The statue of a _____ _____ is in the Boatwrights' parlor.

2. Lily discovers a _____ _____ with tiny pieces of paper in the crevices.

3. The Boatwright sisters kneel before _____ _____

   _____ _____ to pray.

4. May Boatwright hums _____ _____ when she becomes upset.

5. While riding with Zach, Lily experiences emotional extremes of _____ and

   _____.

B. Identification: Match each description with the correct character.

____ 6. August Boatwright   a. wants to marry June

____ 7. June Boatwright   b. committed suicide when she was 15

____ 8. April Boatwright   c. the matriarch of the Boatwright family

____ 9. Neil   d. helps with beekeeping chores

____ 10. Zachary Taylor   e. does not want Lily and Rosaleen to stay with them

C. Open-Ended Comprehension: On the lines below, explain the cause and effect of Lily's fainting spell.

_____

_____

_____

_____

Name _____

A. True/False

____ 1. August first develops an interest in the Black Madonna from her mother's prayer cards.

____ 2. A slave originally found the Boatwrights' statue of the black Mary.

____ 3. August learned about bees and beekeeping from her mother.

____ 4. When Lily calls T. Ray collect, he tells her that he has been worried about her.

____ 5. A water fight ends the hostility between June and Lily.

____ 6. Zach is arrested for hitting a white man in the head with a bottle.

____ 7. Lily mails her father a letter in which she tells him how despicable he is.

____ 8. Lily learns from May that her mother had visited the Boatwrights.

____ 9. Rosaleen's arrest triggers May's suicide.

____ 10. August believes a vigil helps the dead person ascend to heaven.

B. Open-Ended Comprehension: On the lines below, explain the importance of racial prejudice to the plot.

_____

_____

_____

_____

_____

_____

_____

_____

_____

Name _____

A. Fill in the Blanks

1. The Daughters of Mary celebrate Mary Day by chaining _____.

2. August brings Lily a box of _____.

3. T. Ray threatens Lily with a knife because he thinks she is _____.

4. The item of her mother's that Lily most treasures is _____.

5. The "moons" shining over Lily are _____.

B. Identification: Match each description with the correct character.

_____ 6. T. Ray   a. tells Lily Our Lady of Chains is something inside a person

_____ 7. Zach   b. registers to vote

_____ 8. Deborah   c. tells Lily she did cause her mother's death

_____ 9. Rosaleen   d. promises to come back and find Lily someday

_____ 10. August   e. got married because she was pregnant

C. Open-Ended Comprehension: On the following lines, explain the cause/effect of Lily's violent outburst.

_____

_____

_____

_____

_____

_____

_____

_____

Name _____

A. Identification: Match each description with the correct character.

_____ 1. Lily Owens   a. afraid to love because of being jilted

_____ 2. T. Ray Owens   b. persistent in the pursuit of true love

_____ 3. Rosaleen   c. lives under a cloud of guilt and rejection

_____ 4. August Boatwright   d. aspires to become a lawyer

_____ 5. June Boatwright   e. compassionate, understanding beekeeper

_____ 6. May Boatwright   f. negligent, cruel, unloving parent

_____ 7. Zachary Taylor   g. encourages a young black man

_____ 8. Deborah Owens   h. refuses to grovel before racists

_____ 9. Clayton Forrest   i. overwhelmed by the sorrows of the world

_____ 10. Neil   j. subject of a young girl's guilt and yearning

B. Multiple Choice: Select the BEST answer for each item.

_____ 11. Lily's narrative begins the year she turns
     a. 4
     b. 10
     c. 14
     d. 16

_____ 12. The recurring thought from which Lily cannot escape is her
     a. fear of dying
     b. belief that she is ugly
     c. belief that she killed her mother
     d. desire to run away from her father

_____ 13. The punishment that Lily most dreads is
     a. kneeling on grits
     b. being whipped with a switch
     c. not being allowed to watch TV
     d. having her allowance taken away

_____ 14. Rosaleen decides to register to vote
     a. when Lily encourages her to do so
     b. because her minister tells her she should
     c. because she has finally learned to write her name
     d. after seeing President Johnson sign the Civil Rights Act of 1964

_____ 15. Lily chooses Tiburon, South Carolina, as her and Rosaleen's destination because
   a. Rosaleen's relatives live there
   b. she only has enough money to get that far
   c. Lily remembers her mother mentioning the town
   d. she found the name on the back of the Black Madonna picture

_____ 16. Lily and Rosaleen first see August Boatwright
   a. at the general store
   b. working with her bees
   c. going into the pink house
   d. the evening that they arrive in Tiburon

_____ 17. The black Mary statue was originally
   a. bought in Europe
   b. stolen from a church
   c. found in an antique shop
   d. mounted on the front of a ship

_____ 18. When explaining why she and Rosaleen have come to Tiburon, Lily tells the truth
   when she
   a. explains Rosaleen's injuries
   b. explains her father's accident
   c. tells why she is going to Virginia
   d. says that she and Rosaleen ran away

_____ 19. The Boatwright sisters' religion is
   a. based primarily on Catholicism
   b. based primarily on Protestantism
   c. a mixture of Catholic and personal beliefs
   d. a mixture of Catholic and Protestant beliefs

_____ 20. Lily wants to please August
   a. so she will love her
   b. to make more money
   c. to prove she can be trusted
   d. to keep her from calling the police

_____ 21. According to August's story, slaves named the Mary statue "Our Lady of Chains"
   because she
   a. broke her chains
   b. was wrapped in chains
   c. wears beautiful necklaces
   d. made unbreakable chains

_____ 22. Lily realizes her hysterical crying is the result of
   a. missing her father
   b. her feelings for Zach
   c. Zach's inattentiveness
   d. feelings of hopelessness

_____ 23. August puts a picture of the Black Madonna on her honey
   a. to honor her mother
   b. as an act of defiance
   c. because Mary appeared to her in a dream
   d. to show that what is divine can come in dark skin

_____ 24. The pink house symbolizes
   a. June's boldness
   b. May's attempts to be happy
   c. August's ability to choose what matters
   d. the Boatwright sisters' need to be noticed

_____ 25. Lily writes her father a letter
   a. to tell him she loves him
   b. to tell him how despicable he is
   c. because August thinks she should
   d. to try to keep Rosaleen out of trouble

_____ 26. Lily asks Our Lady of Chains to do all BUT which of the following?
   a. fix her
   b. forgive her
   c. let T. Ray love her
   d. send her mother back to her

_____ 27. The conflict between June and Lily ends
   a. during the water fight
   b. after May becomes upset
   c. when Neil proposes to June
   d. when August makes them talk about it

_____ 28. Lily first learns about her mother's presence in the Boatwrights' house from
   a. August
   b. June
   c. May
   d. Neil

_____ 29. Zach is arrested because
    a. he threw a bottle at a black boy
    b. he stole a bottle from a white man
    c. a black boy accuses him of throwing a bottle at a white man
    d. he refuses to tell the police who threw a bottle at a white man

_____ 30. May's suicide is triggered by
    a. her memories of Deborah
    b. June's refusal to marry Neil
    c. learning about Zach's arrest
    d. learning about Rosaleen's arrest

_____ 31. While standing at May's coffin, Lily asks her to
    a. ask God to make T. Ray love her
    b. tell her mother she is sorry for killing her
    c. ask her mother to send a sign of her love
    d. give her the courage to confess everything to August

_____ 32. May's suicide note asks August and June
    a. to bury her by April
    b. not to waste their time to live
    c. to allow Rosaleen to live with them
    d. not to allow anyone to tear down her wall

_____ 33. The Daughters of Mary's celebration of Mary Day is a celebration of
    a. the Assumption
    b. Hanukkah
    c. Kwanzaa
    d. Pentecost

_____ 34. August tells Lily all BUT which one of the following things about her mother?
    a. Lily looks just like her.
    b. She loved to write poetry.
    c. She married T. Ray because she was pregnant with Lily.
    d. She came alone and stayed with the Boatwrights for three months shortly before her death.

_____ 35. Lily reveals to August that one reason she ran away was that
    a. Rosaleen begged her for help
    b. T. Ray threatened her with a knife
    c. T. Ray said her mother deserted them
    d. she discovered how much her father hated her

_____ 36. Lily throws the first jar of honey because
     a. August blames her for killing Deborah
     b. she wants to knock God off His throne
     c. she now knows that no one can love her
     d. she hates seeing the chained statue in the honey house

_____ 37. Which of her mother's possessions is most significant to Lily?
     a. gold pin
     b. hairbrush
     c. pocket mirror
     d. picture of her and her mother

_____ 38. T. Ray is able to find Lily
     a. through a private investigator
     b. by tracing the return address on her letter
     c. because his phone bill shows the location of Lily's collect call
     d. when the Tiburon police department contacts him about a missing person report

_____ 39. T. Ray threatens Lily with a knife
     a. because he thinks she is Deborah
     b. because she tells him she hates him
     c. when she refuses to go home with him
     d. when she accuses him of killing her mother

_____ 40. Which one of the following does NOT occur in the resolution of the plot?
     a. Lily finds a best friend her own age.
     b. T. Ray allows Lily to stay with August.
     c. Lily has many mothers to watch over her.
     d. T. Ray tells Lily that she did not kill her mother.

C. Open-Ended Short Answer Questions: Respond to the following on a separate sheet of paper. Support your answers with evidence from the novel.

(a) Explain the significance of May's wall.

(b) Explain what August tells Lily the statue of Our Lady represents and how this affects Lily.

D. Essay: Respond to one of the following on a separate sheet of paper.

(a) Explain Lily's journey from guilt and anger to forgiveness and acceptance.

(b) Identify and explain one of the following types of conflict in the novel: person vs. person, person vs. self, person vs. society.

(c) August says that human beings' purpose is "not just to love—but to persist in love." Explain how the novel's characters exemplify this purpose.

Name _____

A. Identification: Give three characteristics of Lily Owens, and explain the significance of her quest. Give two characteristics of each character below, and explain his or her significance in Lily's life.

1. Lily Owens _____

_____

_____

2. T. Ray Owens _____

_____

3. Deborah Owens _____

_____

4. Rosaleen _____

_____

5. August Boatwright _____

_____

6. June Boatwright _____

_____

7. May Boatwright _____

_____

8. Zachary Taylor _____

_____

9. Clayton Forrest _____

_____

B. Multiple Choice: Select the BEST answer for each item.

_____ 10. Lily imagines her mother doing all BUT which one of the following when they meet in heaven?
  a. kissing her
  b. fixing her hair
  c. explaining how she really died
  d. telling her she is not to blame for her death

_____ 11. Lily's memories of the day her mother died include all BUT which one of the following?
  a. her parents fighting
  b. firing the gun herself
  c. her mother picking her up
  d. an open suitcase on the floor

_____ 12. Which one of the following is NOT a factor in Lily's low self-esteem?
  a. her father's neglect
  b. abuse from school authorities
  c. no one to guide her through the maturation process
  d. having to wear clothes she makes in home economics

_____ 13. When Lily tells T. Ray she remembers the day her mother died, his reaction implies that he
  a. is not sure what happened
  b. thinks Lily fired the gun deliberately
  c. may be lying about how Deborah died
  d. feels responsible for having a gun in the house

_____ 14. The mental message, "Lily Melissa Owens, your jar is open," is an example of
  a. epiphany
  b. irony
  c. personification
  d. sarcasm

_____ 15. The statement, "(Brother Gerald) loved them in the Lord…but they had their own places," is an example of
  a. ambiguity
  b. epiphany
  c. irony
  d. personification

_____ 16. Lily's and Rosaleen's individual reactions to their arrival at the Boatwright home are best described as
  a. amusement/fear
  b. disappointment/curiosity
  c. excitement/skepticism
  d. nonchalance/anger

_____ 17. Seeing the statue of the black Mary
  a. causes Lily to faint
  b. fills Lily with dread
  c. makes Lily want to go back to Sylvan
  d. causes Lily both to love and hate herself

_____ 18. Repercussions of Lily's fainting include all BUT which one of the following?
  a. May goes to her wailing wall.
  b. June goes to her room and locks the door.
  c. The Daughters of Mary huddle in the kitchen.
  d. August insists on taking Lily to the honey house.

_____ 19. Lily's prayer to the black Mary includes all BUT which one of the following requests?
  a. forgive her
  b. help her stop lying
  c. give her mother a message from her
  d. keep T. Ray and the police from finding her and Rosaleen

_____ 20. August's concern about the length of time the hives are draped after May's death parallels
  a. a person's need to hide from the world while he or she is mourning
  b. the significance of wearing dark clothing for a mourning period of one week
  c. the symbolism of draping all doors and windows during the mourning period
  d. the danger of a person's mourning so long that they can never find a way to happiness and peace

_____ 21. Lily's reaction to August's revelations about Deborah and T. Ray leaves her feeling
  a. as if she finally understands her father
  b. sure that she can never forgive either of them
  c. as if she can finally forgive her mother for leaving
  d. unsure which is heavier to bear, a pack of lies or the truth

_____ 22. Signs that Lily is ready to "live again" include all BUT which one of the following?
  a. She takes an interest in things around her.
  b. She wants to tell Rosaleen she is proud of her and loves her.
  c. She cleans the honey house and displays her mother's things.
  d. She asks August to forgive her for lying and thanks her for all her help.

Name _____

_____ 23. Which one of the following does NOT happen when T. Ray comes for Lily?
a. He tells Lily that she did not kill her mother.
b. Lily realizes how much he loved her mother.
c. August gives him a face-saving way to allow Lily to stay.
d. He threatens her with a knife because he thinks she is Deborah.

C. Literary Devices: On a separate sheet of paper, identify the following (metaphor or simile), state what two things are being compared, and explain the interpretation.

24. "the necklace of lies (Lily) could not stop wearing"

25. "The night seemed like an inkblot (Lily) had to figure out."

D. Open-Ended Short Answer Questions: Respond to the following on a separate sheet of paper. Support your answers with evidence from the book.

26. Identify and explain two examples of "fate" in Lily's quest.

27. Explain the significance of racial strife to the novel's plot and the author's main message.

28. Explain the cause/effect of May's suicide.

29. Explain the significance of Lily's violent outburst.

30. Explain how Lily finally reaches the point of acceptance/forgiveness.

E. Essay: On a separate sheet of paper, complete one of the following in a well-developed essay. Use evidence from the book to support your answer.

(a) Trace the steps of Lily's quest for a mother's love.

(b) Explain the symbolism of the "secret life of bees" and how it affects Lily.

(c) Examine the symbolism of the moon throughout the novel.

Directions: Write a response to the following on a separate sheet of paper. Answer items #1–#3, and choose three to answer from items #4–#8.

1. Explain the importance of the Black Madonna to the plot.

2. Explain the circumstances that caused T. Ray Owens to become an abusive, negligent father and the effect he has on Lily.

3. Identify and analyze the myriad of emotions Lily feels for her mother.

4. Write a metaphorical poem of at least 12 lines about guilt as it is portrayed in the novel.

5. Write Lily's "valedictory" speech at her high school graduation.

6. Write a letter from T. Ray to Lily ten years after the end of the novel.

7. Write a rhyming or free verse poem of at least 12 lines about August Boatwright from Lily's perspective.

8. Write a five-senses poem about one of the novel's themes, e.g., abandonment, rejection, racism, redemption.

Answer Key

Activities #1–#2: Answers will vary.

Activity #3: Charts will vary. Example—Word: brazen; Definition: to face with defiance; Synonym: bold; Antonym: cowardly; Pronunciation: bra'zn; Part of Speech: adjective; Sentence: The student was placed in detention because of his brazen behavior.

Activity #4: Sentences will vary. Example—The team of investigators had a bona fide reason for being on the premises.

Activity #5: Puzzles will vary.

Activity #6: 1. b 2. d 3. a 4. d 5. b 6. a 7. a 8. d 9. c 10. a 11. b 12. d 13. d; Poems/paragraphs will vary.

Study Guide

Chapter 1: 1. Lily Owens; Sylvan, South Carolina, 1964 2. summer of 1964; She turns 14, and her life changes drastically; sent as a sign of impending change 3. "Bees swarm before death"(p. 2); wonders if she will die; Answers will vary. 4. T. Ray Owens; living with him is miserable; does not think he deserves to be called "Dad"; will not allow her to buy pretty clothes, refuses to take her to school functions, ignores her, makes her kneel on grits as punishment 5. the day she died: an open suitcase, fight between her parents, picking up a gun, hearing an explosion; a gunshot wound; T. Ray tells her that she killed her mother; Answers will vary. 6. wears clothes she makes in home economics, has no one to help with her hair; attending charm school; has no white woman to accompany her 7. former peach picker who cooks, cleans, and takes care of Lily; loves her; ways Rosaleen can become her real mother 8. gets angry and refuses to talk about her; picture of her, pair of gloves, small wooden picture of black Mary; buried in the orchard; Answers will vary. 9. Lily's English teacher; tells her she is intelligent enough to become a professor or a writer; Answers will vary. 10. to hold her mother's things; She falls asleep, and T. Ray thinks she has been with a boy. 11. makes her kneel on grits; is appalled and concerned 12. to register to vote; She takes two fans from the church, pours snuff juice on the shoes of racists, and defends herself when she is assaulted. She is charged with assault, theft, and disturbing the peace. 13. Answers will vary.

Chapters 2–3: 1. She is beaten by the same men and taken to the hospital; He, too, is a racist. 2. comes to get her, is furious at her, and threatens severe punishment; Rosaleen's safety; says he doesn't scare her, dodges his blow, tells him her mother will never let him touch her again; Answers will vary. 3. that she ran off and left her; feels "broken to pieces" 4. epiphany: a sudden revelation; believes the bees are telling her to leave 5. to avoid T. Ray's wrath and get Rosaleen out of jail; Tiburon is the city whose name is written on the back of her mother's black Mary picture. 6. to press charges against Rosaleen for stealing fans; She is hard of hearing and misunderstood him. She poured snuff juice on the men's shoes because they asked her to stop singing a hymn; Answers will vary. 7. has been taken to the hospital; finds Rosaleen, devises a way to get her out of the hospital; skeptical, first says she cannot leave 8. hitch a ride in a pickup; Rosaleen thinks Lily treats her like a pet dog; apologize to each other 9. from a general store; snuff; thinks Rosaleen deserves it 10. beekeeper; picture she puts on her jars of honey matches the picture on the card 11. Answers will vary.

Chapters 4–5: 1. Answers will vary. Suggestions: a. compassionate, wise; b. cynical, self-centered; c. peculiar, friendly; August; Answers will vary. 2. about three feet tall, very black, twisted like driftwood, right arm raised and fingers closed in a fist, faded red heart and yellow crescent moon painted on; proud and ashamed; Our Lady of Chains; Answers will vary. 3. fell down the steps; Lily's parents are both dead, and they are on their way to her aunt's home in Virginia; Answers will vary. 4. honey house; Lily works with the bees, and Rosaleen helps May in the house; at peace, does not want to leave 5. Their mother loved spring and summer; May's twin who killed herself 6. the picture of the black Mary and her mother; wants time to win over August so she will not send them back 7. stone wall she built; (a) "Oh! Susanna" (b) small pieces of paper with phrases written on them (c) as a place for May to go when sorrow overwhelms her; (d) Answers will vary, but it is reasonable to say that it is her defense system against all of the pain in the world. 8. believes they are lying and does not want them there; says they are in some kind of trouble and need a place to stay; Answers will vary, but students should mention June's reference to Lily's race. 9. mixture of Catholicism and their own ingredients; starts asking Mary for special help

Chapters 6–7: 1. June's boyfriend; has been jilted before; causes her to go to her wall 2. group of women and one man who celebrate the black Mary; August 3. (a) a slave (b) the statue (c) thinks she was sent by God but does not know who she is (d) takes her to the praise house (e) Mary, the mother of Jesus (f) because she broke her chains 4. June stops the music just as it is Lily's turn to touch the statue's heart; Rosaleen and August take care of her, May goes to her wall, June goes to her room, the Daughters huddle in the kitchen; touch Our Lady's heart; Answers will vary. 5. August's beekeeping helper; lawyer; have an instant rapport 6. She has not touched the statue's heart; Answers will vary. 7. anxiety, hysterical happiness and sadness; overwhelmed by intense feelings for Zach 8. so she can move into May's room; feels deserted and lonely 9. have a falling-out because June will not marry him; Answers will vary. 10. notebook; They are different races.

Chapter 8: 1. Black Madonna of Breznichar in Bohemia; from her mother's prayer cards; to show that "what's divine can come in dark skin" 2. Rosaleen, writing stories, salted peanuts in Coca-Cola, the color blue; her mother's picture and the Black Madonna picture; Answers will vary. 3. almost 18 years; her grandmother; housekeeper, later a teacher 4. letting May choose the color of the house; Answers will vary. 5. nest builders, field bees, morticians, nurses, drones, the queen and her attendants; She lays all the eggs. 6. mentally sends them love; making her immune to hurt, accepting and comforting her; Answers will vary. 7. that Jack Palance will be bringing a black woman to the movie theater; upset, plan to guard the theater 8. a lawyer; to deliver honey; She disapproves. 9. calls him collect; with anger, threatens her; Answers will vary. 10. tells him how despicable he is and that she does not think her mother left her; Answers will vary. 11. fix her, help her know what to do, forgive her, not let "them" find her and Rosaleen or let them take her back to Sylvan, keep Rosaleen from being killed, let T. Ray love her, help her stop lying, and take the meanness out of people; Answers will vary.

Chapter 9: 1. getting stung 2. Rosaleen and May; ends conflict between them 3. elevator; Answers will vary, but students should mention that she feels that she has lied to make herself appear better than she is. 4. the way May leads roaches out of the house; feels lightheaded and trembles 5. the revelation that her mother had been at the Boatwrights' house and the dream in which her mother has cockroach legs; talk to August; August is busy talking to Sugar-Girl, and Lily goes to town with Zach. 6. Friday; the day that Jack Palance is supposed to take a black woman to the theater 7. refuses to reveal who threw the bottle that cut a white man; walks home; distressed, wants to get him out on bail 8. They are afraid it will be too much for her to bear; Answers will vary. 9. August and Lily; write his story; Answers will vary. 10. answers a phone call from Zach's mother; goes into a trance-like state of mind, insists on going by herself to the wall 11. Answers will vary.

Chapter 10: 1. her wall; call the police 2. in the river; a heavy rock on her chest 3. Lily: shivers, teeth chatter, nausea/vomits; August and June: heartbroken acceptance, August with a piercing cry; Rosaleen: silent, shaking uncontrollably; love and anguish for others 4. Answers will vary. 5. He implies that a white girl should not be living with a black family and says that Lily is "lowering herself." He suggests that she should leave as soon as possible. 6. sitting with a dead person until the burial; to allow everyone to say goodbye and to help May's soul ascend to heaven 7. girl who sells movie tickets reveals who threw the bottle; has become angry and cynical and has lost his joy and serenity 8. thinks he should have avoided jail by telling who threw the bottle; tells him that she could just as easily blame herself and that the truth is that May is responsible; Answers will vary. 9. to keep the bees from leaving because having bees around is supposed to ensure that the dead person will live again; Answers will vary. 10. No one thinks of her as different during the vigil; Everybody should be colorless. 11. August; tired of carrying the weight of the world; Answers will vary. 12. four days; take the black cloths off of the hives; Answers will vary but should relate back to Lily's inability to stop mourning her mother's death.

Chapters 11–12: 1. August's mourning period 2. change the world; Answers will vary. 3. a week; everyone eats together, talking and smiling; move back to the honey house 4. feed each other bites of honey cakes, reenact the story of the statue; no conflict, June feeds Lily and apologizes to her 5. She is more devoted to him and agrees to marry him; May's wish for her sisters to "live" 6. chain her in the honey house for the night; to the river; when boys made her wear a necklace of fish; He is sometimes so angry he wants to kill something. 7. nervous, as if she is doomed; taken care of by August, loved dolls, came to Sylvan and fell in love with T. Ray, married him because she was pregnant, stayed with August for three months shortly before her death; Answers will vary. 8. telling August that T. Ray said her mother left her; holds Lily and tells her to cry it out 9. thinks she is a bad person who tells lies, hates people, does all the wrong things, is unlovable; thinks she killed her mother; tells Lily it was an accident and reminds her of everyone who loves her 10. lonely and depressed over marriage; Answers will vary. 11. learns that Deborah came to Tiburon without her; She tells Lily that depressed people do things they would not ordinarily do and reminds Lily that Deborah eventually went back to Sylvan to get her 12. "Left you"; Answers will vary.

Chapters 13–14: 1. throw jars of honey, a bucket, and a tray of candle molds; tired and empty; Answers will vary. 2. Rosaleen; She found out that her mother did leave her; She suspected this because she had heard things about Deborah's departure. 3. be raised from the dead; A big part of her feels dead. 4. her mother's pocket mirror, hairbrush, gold pin, and a picture of Lily and her mother; the picture; It is the sign of love for which she has been waiting. 5. an ice sculpture; Answers will vary. 6. Answers will vary; her mother 7. puts her mother's things under her cot and carries the bones in her pocket; Answers will vary. 8. She is not a magical being but something inside you that gives you strength. 9. traces her collect phone call and finds out where she is from Mr. Forrest's secretary; intends to take her home with him; Lily looks like Deborah, and his repressed grief resurfaces. He momentarily thinks it is ten years ago and that Deborah is leaving him; brings him back to reality by calling him "Daddy" 10. tells him they love her, need her help, will take care of her, and start her in school there 11. if she actually killed her mother; did not mean to but yes; Answers will vary. 12. (a) keeps imagining her father will let her know he loves her (b) Mr. Forrest is working to get them dropped. (c) becomes Lily's first female teenage friend (d) her "many mothers"

Note: Responses to Activities #7–#15 will vary. Suggested responses are given where applicable.

Activity #7: Lily Owens—Beginning: insecure, low self-esteem, guilt-ridden; Event #1: Flashbacks reveal her longing for her mother and guilt for causing her death: depressed; Event #2: Rosaleen is arrested: anxious; Event #3: She and Rosaleen escape and go to Tiburon: apprehensive yet liberated; Event #4: She stays with August and learns about beekeeping and the Black Madonna: content and anxious (in cycles); Event #5: Her father finds her and threatens her: fearful yet strong; Event #6: T. Ray allows her to stay: relieved; End: She accepts her mother's death and forgives herself and her mother: free, at peace

Activity #8: (1) mentally relives day her mother died; (2) decides to go to Tiburon to learn more about her mother and help Rosaleen escape; (3) accepted and loved by August; (4) confesses her "crime" to August; (5) reacts violently when she learns her mother left her; (6) realizes her mother was flawed but loved her, accepts and forgives herself and her mother

Activity #9: Lily: insecure, alienated, lonely, eventually loved; T. Ray: negligent, cruel, demanding, intolerant; Rosaleen: devoted, strong, determined, conscientious; Zach: handsome, caring, hardworking, ambitious; August: industrious, loving, compassionate, charitable; Lily/T. Ray: wants him to love her; unconcerned about her needs; Lily/Rosaleen: concerned, loving; sympathetic, protective; Lily/Zach: mutually understanding and affectionate; Lily/August: admires her; accepts her

Activity #10: Causes: father's negligence, rejected by peers, having to wear homemade clothes, father's cruel punishment, guilt over her mother's death, needing a mother to love and protect her

Activity #11: Character: Lily, Conflict: believes she killed her mother, Resolution: August helps her accept her mother's death and forgive herself and her mother; Character: Rosaleen, Conflict: arrested and beaten because of racial discrimination, Resolution: She escapes with Lily to Tiburon; Character: T. Ray, Conflict: refuses to talk to Lily about her mother, punishes and controls her, Resolution: August talks him into letting Lily stay in Tiburon.

Activity #12: Problem: T. Ray's rage over Lily and Rosaleen's arrest; Solution: Lily decides to run away; Problem: Lily needs a place to go; Solution: decides on Tiburon because of Black Madonna picture; Problem: May feels overwhelming sorrow for world's problems; Solution: August and June send her to her wailing wall; Problem: Zach sees who throws a bottle at a white man; Solution: refuses to reveal the perpetrator; Problem: May's sorrows become too great for her to bear; Solution: commits suicide; Problem: June does not want Lily and Rosaleen to stay; Solution: August insists that they can.

Activity #13: Characters: Lily Owens, T. Ray, Rosaleen, Boatwright sisters, Zach, Neil, Daughters of Mary; Time and Place: Sylvan and Tiburon, South Carolina, 1964; Problem: Lily searches for answers about her mother; Goal: to be able to forgive herself and find a "mother"; Episodes: (1) Lily and Rosaleen run away from Sylvan to escape T. Ray and violent racists. (2) They go to Tiburon, where they find refuge and answers from August Boatwright. (3) Lily accepts the truth about her mother and discovers her inner strength; Resolution: She forgives Deborah and herself and realizes she has many mothers.

Activity #14: 1. Lily 2. Rosaleen, bees, mother's things 3. time, assistance, friendship 4. love, father's attention, forgiveness 5. information about her mother, resolution of her guilt, a loving home 6. academics, beekeeping, writing 7. self-image, telling the truth, forgiving herself 8. Zach, Rosaleen (both mistreated), her mother 9. father's cruelty, peer rejection, not having a mother 10. Owens

Activity #15: Theme: persisting in love: Lily forgives her mother; Lily becomes aware of and overcomes her prejudice; June overcomes her prejudice and learns to love Lily; June decides to marry Neil though she fears being jilted; Lily's hope that T. Ray will express love for her; August's love of Lily regardless of her lies; Zach and Lily's continued love/friendship despite society's disapproval; May's sweetness and compassion despite her inner pain; Main message: Within every person is the inner strength to fulfill humanity's great purpose, persisting in love.

Quiz #1: A. 1. 3 2. 5 3. 1 4. 4 5. 2 **B.** 6. F 7. T 8. T 9. F 10. F **C.** Answers will vary. Refer to the scoring rubric on page 44 of this guide.

Quiz #2: A. 1. black Mary/Black Madonna 2. stone/wailing wall 3. Our Lady of Chains 4. "Oh! Susanna" 5. laughing/happiness; crying/sadness **B.** 6. c 7. e 8. b 9. a 10. d **C.** Answers will vary. Refer to the scoring rubric on page 44 of this guide.

Quiz #3: A. 1. T 2. T 3. F 4. F 5. T 6. F 7. F 8. T 9. F 10. T **B.** Answers will vary. Refer to the scoring rubric on page 44 of this guide.

Quiz #4: A. Our Lady of Chains 2. her mother's things 3. Deborah 4. a picture of her and her mother 5. her many mothers **B.** 6. c 7. d 8. e 9. b 10. a **C.** Answers will vary. Refer to the scoring rubric on page 44 of this guide.

Novel Test, Level One: A. 1. c 2. f 3. h 4. e 5. a 6. i 7. d 8. j 9. g 10. b **B.** 11. c 12. c 13. a 14. d 15. d 16. b 17. d 18. d 19. c 20. a 21. a 22. b 23. d 24. c 25. b 26. d 27. a 28. c 29. d 30. c 31. c 32. b 33. a 34. b 35. c 36. b 37. d 38. c 39. a 40. d **C.** Answers will vary. Refer to the scoring rubric on page 44 of this guide. Suggestions: (a) writing down her sorrows and putting them in the wall provides relief because it is a form of mourning; the notes are her way of attempting to hand her worries to God (b) something inside each person that gives him or her strength and consolation; Lily realizes this is the strength that helped her survive her father's cruelty and eventually finds the strength to stand up to him. **D.** Responses will vary. Refer to the scoring rubric on page 44 of this guide.

Novel Test, Level Two: A. 1. low self-esteem, yearns for her mother's love, blames herself for killing her mother; searching for closure to her mother's death and forgiveness for her role in that death, searching for a mother's love 2. cruel, demanding, self-centered; negligent father and reason for her low self-esteem 3. beautiful, lonely, depressed; her mother whom Lily thinks she killed 4. kind, courageous, loving; has taken care of her since her mother's death 5. compassionate, wise, patient; becomes Lily's confidante and helps her find healing and inner strength 6. self-centered, unsympathetic, learns to love; initially resents but later accepts Lily 7. depressed, sensitive, perceptive; first to tell Lily that her mother stayed with them 8. brave, handsome, ambitious; co-worker and love interest 9. kind, loyal, helpful; works to resolve Sylvan charges **B.** 10. c 11. b 12. b 13. c 14. a 15. c 16. c 17. d 18. d 19. c 20. d 21. d 22. d 23. a **C.** 24. metaphor; lies: necklace; One might use a necklace to enhance one's beauty. Lily feels that she uses her lies to appear to be better than she is. 25. simile; night: inkblot; Lily's loneliness and doubt are reflected in the night sky, from which the moon (symbolic of her mother) is absent. She stares out into the darkness trying to figure out the best way to get the answers she needs about her mother. **D.** Answers will vary. Refer to the scoring rubric on page 44 of this guide. Suggestions: 26. The bees that Lily captured finally decide to leave the open jar. This inspires Lily to run away to Tiburon, where she starts her new, bee-oriented life; Lily sees a label on a jar of honey that is the same Black Madonna picture as the one on her mother's card. This leads her to August Boatwright. 27. In another place and time, Rosaleen and Zach would not have been arrested. Lily may not have taken Rosaleen with her to Tiburon, and May may not have committed suicide. The novel's tension and conflict, as well as the author's message of persisting in love, would have been diluted. 28. Cause: May learns of Zach's arrest. Effect: She reacts differently than before. Cause: She insists on going to the wall by herself. Effect: She is able to kill herself. Cause: August discovers May's suicide note. Effect: June is convinced to "live," and she marries Neil. 29. shows her anger and disillusionment at finding out that her mother did desert her for three months 30. overhears August's comment that regrets do not help anything, realizes that others are going on with their lives and begins to be more concerned about them than herself, tells Rosaleen she loves her, displays her mother's things **E.** Answers will vary. Refer to the scoring rubric on page 44 of this guide.

Alternative Assessment: Answers will vary. Refer to the scoring rubric on page 44 of this guide. Suggestions: 1. leads Lily to her many mothers, helps her cope with heartache, accept her mother's death, and stand up to her father by enabling her to realize her inner strength 2. Deborah's desertion and death left T. Ray with feelings of inadequacy and trust and control issues. He sees Lily as a burden and the living remnant of his relationship with Deborah. T. Ray copes with his emotional issues through his harsh discipline and neglect of Lily. His behavior is the reason for Lily's low self-esteem. 3. love for the girl in the picture, grief and guilt over her death, anger over being deserted, yearning for her love #4–#8: Answers will vary.

Linking Novel Units® Student Packets to National and State Reading Assessments

During the past several years, an increasing number of students have faced some form of state-mandated competency testing in reading. Many states now administer state-developed assessments to measure the skills and knowledge emphasized in their particular reading curriculum. This Novel Units® guide includes open-ended comprehension questions that correlate with state-mandated reading assessments. The rubric below provides important information for evaluating responses to open-ended comprehension questions. Teachers may also use scoring rubrics provided for their own state's competency test.

Scoring Rubric for Open-Ended Items

3-Exemplary
Thorough, complete ideas/information
Clear organization throughout
Logical reasoning/conclusions
Thorough understanding of reading task
Accurate, complete response

2-Sufficient
Many relevant ideas/pieces of information
Clear organization throughout most of response
Minor problems in logical reasoning/conclusions
General understanding of reading task
Generally accurate and complete response

1-Partially Sufficient
Minimally relevant ideas/information
Obvious gaps in organization
Obvious problems in logical reasoning/conclusions
Minimal understanding of reading task
Inaccuracies/incomplete response

0-Insufficient
Irrelevant ideas/information
No coherent organization
Major problems in logical reasoning/conclusions
Little or no understanding of reading task
Generally inaccurate/incomplete response